Shann...

dick bruna

miffy
in
hospital

TED SMART

Said Miffy to her mum one day

I don't feel very strong

and now my throat feels funny, too

what do you think is wrong?

I'm not sure, her mother said

but this is what we'll do:

we'll go and find the doctor, and

see what he thinks of you.

The doctor said: yes, there's the spot

we'll take the pain away

I'll do it at the hospital –

we'd better go today.

The hospital? Poor Miffy squeaked

but won't it hurt a lot?

and do I have to go alone?

I think I'd rather not ...

No, Miffy would not be alone

her mum would take her there

and in her little case she packed

the nightdress she would wear.

But when they reached the hospital:

it's so big! Miffy said

I don't think it looks very nice

can I go home instead?

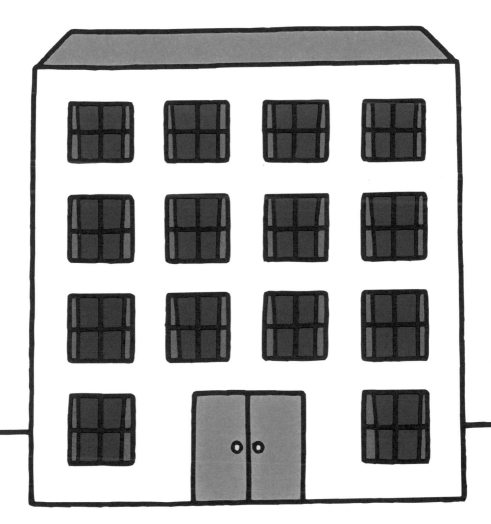

Ah, look! a nurse was coming out

Miffy, hello! she said

I'm glad to see you, hold my hand,

I'll show you to your bed.

Miffy was tucked up in her bed,

the room was brightly lit

Nurse put a needle in her arm

it scarcely hurt a bit.

That little prick made Miffy feel

so tired, her eyelids closed

I'm very sleepy, Miffy thought,

and fell into a doze.

When Miffy woke, what did she find?

she didn't feel so sick,

and Nurse was saying: you're better now

my goodness, that was quick!

That afternoon, her Mother came,

and Father Bunny, too

how are you, Miffy? look we've got

a present here for you!

It was a doll, a proper nurse,

and Miffy hugged her tight

that's great! said Miffy, hospital

is really quite all right.

miffy's library

miffy
miffy's dream
miffy goes to stay
miffy is crying
miffy at the seaside
miffy at school

miffy at the playground
miffy in hospital
miffy's bicycle
miffy at the gallery
miffy's birthday
miffy the fairy

miffy's garden
miffy and the new baby
dear grandma bunny
miffy at the zoo

"nijntje in het ziekenhuis"
Produced in Great Britain 2006 for The Book People Ltd, Hall Wood Avenue,
Haydock, St Helens WA11 9UL by Egmont UK Limited, 239 Kensington
High Street, London W8 6SA.
Publication licensed by Mercis Publishing bv, Amsterdam
Original text Dick Bruna © copyright Mercis Publishing bv, 1975
Illustrations Dick Bruna © copyright Mercis bv, 1975
Original English translation © copyright Patricia Crampton, 1996
The moral right of the author has been asserted.
Printed in China
10 9 8 7 6 5 4 3 2 1